OF

OPEN WIDE

by

MATTHEW FINCH
(author of *Dentist in the Chair*,
Teething Troubles, etc., etc.)

and

BILL TIDY

London
DENNIS DOBSON

The author offers many thanks to H. Colin Davis,
for *Dental News and Dental Practice*;
BBC Television and radio; *Granada Television*;
Radio Merseyside; *The Liverpool Echo*;
Lancashire Life where this material first appeared

First published in Great Britain in 1976 by
Dobson Books Ltd, 80 Kensington Church Street,
London W8
Printed in Great Britain by
Chelsea Printing Services Ltd,
186 Campden Hill Road, London W8 7TH

ISBN 0 234 77430 4

OPENING UP

I suspect it's going to be one of *those* days. I arrive ten minutes late at the surgery. The receptionist has given the first appointment to two different (and angry) patients. "Don't worry," I tell her. "We all make mistakes. Nobody's perfect."

She hurries off into the cupboard we use as a dark room. I hear her sniffing and sobbing. I'm angry with myself for having behaved like a pig. The surgery attendant stands poker faced. My petulant little foot stamps on the floor. "I *hate* starting work knowing that I'm forty minutes late before I even put on my white coat."

Poker face ushers in the first patient. There's a forced sweet smile hanging over my sour cheeks, like a surgical mask. "Let's do something easy today," I suggest, hoping to catch up time.

"Just do this one," the patient says, pointing to a front tooth. "It's been aching me." (And who else?) I sense it's going to be a long job. It is. Forty minutes later, the second patient is led in, holding his wrist watch to his ear. "Sorry to keep you waiting," I apologise. "Let's do something easy today."

The receptionist tip-toes in, nibbling the corner of a record card. "There's a Mrs Clack on the 'phone. . ."

"Not *her* again. She's always here. Tell her I'll only see her today if she's in pain."

"She's just fallen over and knocked the top off one of her teeth. She says it's killing her."

I want to scream, but one never does. "Tell her to come now. Tell her I'm hours late, and she may have to wait all night."

The door bell rings before I can start work on the patient. "If it's anyone without an appointment," I shout, "just don't tell me. I don't want to know." Then the telephone rings. Door bell and telephone bell play a discordant carillon together. I feel anger and gastric juice rising to throat level. "When the next bell rings, I'm going to start screaming," I tell the patient as I thrust the hypodermic at him.

The receptionist pokes her head into the surgery. "Mr Flicker's at the door. Got a face like a football."

"Then what's he want? Someone to kick it? He's come to the right place, I'm in the mood."

"Shall I send him away, then?" she asks quietly.

I abandon all hope of catching up on time. "No. Let him stay. Tell him he'll have to wait for hours and days and weeks and. . ." The door bell rings whilst I'm ranting away. The receptionist runs off. "Don't open that door!" I shout after her.

She ignores me. She always does. She comes back. "It's a traveller from Central Chemicals."

"Tell him he can go to Hell, bloody Hell if you like."

She produces a box of free samples from behind her back. "He brought these headache pills for you, you were in such a state last time he came."

I give up. My shoulders droop into the rounded

6

stance of a tired, old dentist who knows he's top of the Registrar-General's statistics for death-rate. "O.K. let *him* stay. Put him on top of the pile in the waiting room — but give me a couple of those pills of his first before my headache starts. I can see it's going to be one of *those* days."

"What d'you mean?" she asks, helping herself to the tablets, too. "One of *those* days? It's like this *every* day."

IT'S AN EMERGENCY

I'll tell you what an emergency is. It means someone's got toothache and they have no appointment, so someone fondly expects to be fitted in at once and everyone else can go to hell.

The receptionist comes in. "Mrs Er says her son's orthodontic plate is causing trouble and you'll *have* to see him *right away* because . . ."

". . . it's an emergency," I finish it for her. "O.K. then, fit him in sometime tomorrow. But — don't tell me when, just let it come as a surprise."

"But Mrs Er says it *can't* wait." (She steps back so that I can't lash out at her with something — or anything.)

I gnash my teeth. "I'll just have to give up a bit of my dinner time. I'm getting too fat anyway."

The receptionist hesitates. "Well, actually, Mrs Er says that this afternoon would be just a teensy-weensy bit more convenient for her."

"For *her?*" My voice rises in pitch and volume. "We've already got three extra this afternoon, from yesterday. Tell her to go and . . ."

It seems only a few seconds later that there are three long rings at the doorbell. Three denotes character, I suppose. I can hear Mrs Er braying "I hope he's not going to keep *me* waiting too. I'm a *very* busy woman." Her cigarette case clicks. It means she's going to walk into the surgery smoking — as usual.

I point at the cigarette when she comes in. "D'you mind?"

"And do I mind what?" She turns my request into an indecent suggestion.

"Your cigarette. In the surgery. Hygiene, sort of thing."

She just flicks ash on the floor. You'd think I hadn't spoken. "It's Robin. He's got himself all mixed up with your orthodontic thing." He's standing there with a scarf wrapped round his face. He seems to have grown a snout but, when Mrs Er unrolls the scarf, I see it isn't a snout. It's a collection of metal rods hanging from his mouth like ferrous macaroni.

"Surely that's no my orthodontic plate?" I ask. "What's he been eating? Meccano?"

Mrs Er sucks her cigarette and exhales to the side as a token gesture to hygiene. "It's a carburettor," she explains. "One of the cars broke down when I was taking Robin to College this morning. It was an emergency." (It always is — for some people). "So I rang the R.A.C. and whilst their chappy was footling around with the engine, Robin leaned over the bonnet to watch. So — ah — to cut a long story short," (it never does) "poor Robin somehow slipped forward and got his brace caught on the carburettor, and we couldn't unhook him. R.A.C. chappy said it was agin his bleddy Union rules to touch it. So we had to fetch the fire brigade along to deal with the emergency," naturally, "they're used to children stuck in railings and things. They had to unbolt some of the carburettor, so there it is. And now may I use your telephone?"

I'm busy disentangling reciprocating rods and cam-shafts from what is left of Robin's brace. I hear his mother braying *"Taxi! Taxi!"* down the telephone. *"This is an emergency!"*

It always is for some people, Jack.

SCREWED INTO ME GUM

"Now," she says, leaning back in the chair, "I'll have 'em out and in, in one go."

"Beg your pardon?" I think I've misheard.

"And I've taken the day off work specially," she adds.

"I hope you don't expect any treatment today. All I do at the first visit is to examine your teeth. You may not need any treatment."

"I'll have 'em all out," she nods, "with The Gas, of course. And then you can screw in some new teeth before I wake up."

My receptionist emits a strangled cry at the magic words *screwing in*. She knows it just doesn't exist — it's a dental folk-legend — and people ask for "screwing in" (or sometimes just "screwing") almost daily. From behind the dental chair she waves me a warning not to hit the patient. She picks up a match-box and goes through the motions of *striking off*.

"I'm sorry, but there's no such thing as screwing teeth into your gum." There is a controlled explosive feeling as I speak, like driving with the brakes on.

"Of course there is!" Her face says thank God I know something about dentistry, even if this chap doesn't.

"Sorry! *No!*" This chap shakes his head.

"Oh pardon me but *yes!*" She nods just as vigorously. "My friend had it done by a chap in Piccadilly and she'd been gummy for years. Mind

11

you," she sniffs, "her chap was a dental *surgeon*, of course."

I could hit her for saying "of course". "And I suppose she had a full top and bottom set screwed into her gums before she woke up." There's nothing like the old acid to put vinegar pusses in their places.

"*Exactly!*" She nods again.

"Well — let *me* tell *you*," I'm driving with the brakes off now, "you just *can't* have that done. Your friend was toothless and would have needed natural tooth-roots (at least) before new teeth could be screwed in, as you called it. Actually, new teeth aren't screwed into bare gum, they have to be fixed on the old roots."

"I know all about that." She waves a dismissing hand. "And so does this dental *surgeon* in Piccadilly. When he found that my friend had no teeth of her own, he just opened his drawers and took out some old roots and screwed them into her straight away. Now," she leans back in the dental chair, "just you do the same for me."

NO PLACE LIKE HOME –
or His little head's all hot

"You'll have to wait a minute, his poor little head's gone all hot." Mrs Er appears in the doorway. Behind her, in the waiting room, a little foot is stamping. "No! No! No!" screams a small voice, anything but still. Now she's trying to drag her child into the surgery. "Ah! His little head's gone all hot again."

I know what she means. Every time he comes, his little head goes hot and he's never even got as far as the chair. His poor little record card records four separate visits as "Examination Refused". At the top of the card, in the space marked "Clinical Notes" I have written *"Little Sod"*.

Mrs Er wheedles her child inside. She promises to buy him his own toy shop if only he'll let the man just even look at his peggies. "I know what to do!" I suggest. "Let's put the telly on. Perhaps it'll make him feel more at home."

The picture lights up to show someone spouting to schools about the Differential Calculus. *"No!"* shouts little hot-head. "I hate *them* and all."

Can't say I blame him, either. "How about this then? You stand where you are, and I'll come over and look at your teeth while you hold mummy's hand."

The yelling mouth snaps shut and a little hand is clapped across it. Mrs Er phrenologises him again. "Oo! His little head's going all hot again." She

13

whispers through the side of her mouth like they do in cowboy pictures. "He's such a sensitive child, you see."

Sensitive child hears every word. He stands there red-faced as a monkey's bottom, sticking his tongue out at me. "Oo!" says Mrs Er. "Stoppit at *once*, Grainger, or I'll tell Daddy the very instant he comes home tonight." Sensitive child starts to kick the megavolts out of my X-Ray machine; he pulls his tongue in. "That's better," says Mrs Er, "he's really *such* a good boy, and perhaps he's ready to sit on the chair now."

My professional mask slips. "About time, too!" It uncovers the rotten, impatient, frustrated human being under the dentist's white coat. "I mean, after all, this is his fourth visit and I don't even know if he's got any teeth."

"Indeed?" Mrs Er asks nastily. "Which is more important, your precious time, or the proper handling of a poor defenceless child? You're not very helpful, are you? Why don't you just get hold of him and do him like his last dentist used to do?"

My receptionist waves a hand. She's imploring me not to answer; she can see that my little head's going all hot too. "I'm damned if I'm going to use brute force on any patient — especially on your little xxxxxx." There! I think. I've actually been and gone and *done it*. After twenty-five years of wanting to call someone a xxxxxx, I've actually done it (and dentists have been struck off for xxxx — or even xxx).

Funny? Nothing happens. The child comes across to sit in the chair. I even do a small filling. Amazing. "What came over him?" I ask his mother.

She smiles at me. "You said just the right thing! His daddy *always* calls him a little xxxxx, so when you called him one too, it made him feel at home at last. Mind you," she adds, whispering out of the side of her mouth again, "his little head's still all hot, so I'd work fast if I were you."

TOO MANY HANDS – TOO MANY COOKS

In goes the gold filling. I test the edge for a good fit. I lift up a thingy to polish the gold into place. Holding the filling in the tooth with one hand, I jiggle the polishing thingy about with the other. The polisher buzzes round and round until suddenly there's a click. The gold filling is flicked out of the tooth and blasts off into orbit because the electric polishing thingy has gone mad and has started to turn the wrong way.

I spend ten furious minutes playing kneesy-kneesy on the floor with my receptionist before we find the gold filling. While it's cooking in the steriliser, I go and kick hell out of the dental engine's foot-control to see why it's turning the wrong way. I tell the patient that normal service will be resumed very shortly. It's the understatement of the year.

The electric engine comes to pieces. Black-handed I poke at it and find no visible defect, so I reassemble it and cross my black fingers. The thing still turns the wrong way. "Better get that damn fellow on the 'phone!" I shout.

She knows who I mean. He comes at once, too. He pokes at the engine and then crosses *his* black fingers. This time, nothing at all happens. "I'll have to take it away," he says.

The patient frowns at his watch and sucks at the hole in his tooth. "I'm an electrical engineer. D'you mind if I have a go?" He kneels down and fiddles with armatures and brushes and brass springs. "Just you try a bit of vaseline in there," he says, pointing at something. The receptionist hands him a dollop on a glass slab. He dabs a little finger in it and then smears a bit of vaseline on there. Then he puts all the bits together again. "Now, what d'you bet there'll be a bloody big bang and all the lights go out?" he asks, all cocky. We laugh, of course.

We wish we'd taken his bet. There *is* a bloody big bang and all the lights do go out. The regular repair man giggles with Schadenfreude.

"Can't understand it!" the chagrined expert mutters. Then the receptionist nudges me and points, red-faced, at the jar she'd thought contained vaseline. The label says *"Water soluble grease. Not to be used on insulated electrical contacts."*

Soon, all is well. We're only an hour late, so bang goes lunchtime again. The patient is tapping his wristwatch as I start up the polishing thingy again. But I'm too hurried to notice that I've got it turning the wrong way again, at maximum revs, and all. The filling blasts off into orbit once more. This time, splash-down is in the wash basin. It plunks straight down the plug-hole, Hole in One, the Golden Shot.

Clutching my few remaining hairs, I turn to the patient. "Are you any good at unscrewing U-bends, too?" I whisper, teeth all clenched.

POOR RETENTION –
or Cyrano de Buggerlugs

The receptionist comes in and leans against the wall, her eyes rolling with feigned love-sickness. "Cyrano's come," she whispers. She has evocative names for all her favourite patients. "Cyrano's definitely top of my list!" She clicks an appreciative tongue as if at a horse. "He's a *real* buggerlugs." (And beware all imitation ones.)

"Which one's Cyrano de Buggerlugs, then?" I ask.

"He's that lovely, dishy man with the big, sexy nose and wavy hair like a thick black sea." Then she goes and ushers him in, big nose, black thatch and a gold front tooth. He's touching her hand for no apparent reason. "Thank *you*, dear," he says, sitting in the chair.

I want to ask him if he'd rather have *her* working on him today, instead of me, but settle for a weak, "Let's see what's next."

"Don't even bother to look," Cyrano orders me around. "We'll be doing that one at the front today." He picks up the tumbler of mouthwash, says "Cheers" to nobody in particular, and has a pre-emptive gargle. Twitching his lovely, big, sexy nose at my receptionist, he points to an upper front tooth.

I tell him that there are several much more urgent further back.

"Maybe," he agrees, "but we'll be doing this one today, just the same."

18

I want to slap him on the head with a pair of tweezers. I want to tell him that he doesn't need to remind *us* of *our* professional duty. I want to ask him please not to make nasal love to my staff, it gets them ga-ga for the rest of the day. *But*, I remember the Dental Council, with its power to strike my name from the list of people with the highest death rate of any profession. (Perhaps I ought to let them do it so's I can live longer.)

The drill head is air-blasting away inside his

mouth. Suddenly — without a how-d'you-do — up comes Cyrano's hand and brushes it all aside. "We're getting that lot right up our nose," he says, gripping my wrist. "Haven't you got anything less breath-taking?"

The answer trembling on my lips threatens to take away his breath altogether. "You mustn't ever grab at high-speed instruments, mate!" I snap back. "You could slice your face open — or worse."

A movement catches my eye. My receptionist is standing behind Cyrano, pointing at his hair — the thick, black sea. She puts a finger in her mouth and mimes a Red Indian yell. I think she's gone "Must" like a randy elephantess. She points again at the patient's head. I see I have scalped him.

His thick, black thatch rises vertically from his crown, like the lifted toecap of a cartoon tramp's boot. Beneath the dark, wavy bushel, an honest bald head flashes the light of truth.

The tables are turned, the wig is on the other foot. "Excuse me," I whisper, happily cruel. "The air blast from *our* drill has disturbed *our* toupée."

He still comes for treatment, of course, but my receptionist says he's no longer top of her list. She suspects that his lovely, sexy nose is probably false too — so she just calls him Buggerlugs now.

THREE QUID PRO QUO

"Oh yes!" says Mr Boo, sitting down in the dental chair. "Your waiting room could certainly do with a lick of paint."

"But it was only done last August!" I protest.

"Bum job," says Mr Boo. "I'm a decorator. I notice these things." He's scrutinising the surgery ceiling as he talks. "And you've lost your key up there, you know."

"What key?" I wonder if there's a notice up there saying "April Fool". "I haven't lost any key." I squint up to see what exactly *is* on the ceiling.

Mr Boo points. "Your plaster isn't keyed into your laths up there."

"Are you saying that the ceiling's about to fall down?"

He nods. "Definitely."

I fetch a broom handle and gently tap the plaster. It feels solid as a bollard. "This won't fall down in the next fifty years!"

"It *will*, you know, if you thump it like that," he sniggers. "And your waiting room still needs a lick of paint even if it was done last August. Whoever done it, he twisted you."

Next visit, it's the same thing all over again, except this time it's the doors he's gone mad on. The lintels are all gozzy (whatever that means). Then, he's back on the unpainted waiting room walls again.

Two weeks later, the wood block floor turns

out to be cheap rubbish, and the central heating — laugh! — it's only been thrown together. Then the windows — *out* of skew (or was it *in* skew). The skirting boards were sodden with damp too ("like sponges. You c'd use them in your bath" — a quaint thought) *and* of course, my waiting room was rapidly falling into the delapidation of the great unlicked.

"All right then!" I snap back, biting the biter. "I suppose you could make a better job of the waiting room?"

"Me?" Mr Boo spreadeagles a hand on his bosom. "I'd even give you a guarantee." He has his estimate ready, no measuring up needed. "Burn off, rub down, fill in, primer, undercoat, two gloss, forty-eight and a half."

"You're on!" I tell him as he signs off at the end of his treatment. "You owe the National Health three pounds, and when can you start painting the waiting room?"

"How about this weekend? Tell you what," Mr Boo suggests, fumbling in his pocket and finding no money. "You take the three quid off my bill. Just call it forty-five and a half you owe me. Save all that messing about, me to you and then back to me again."

Weak minded as always, I agree to it all.

Come Friday evening, we empty the waiting room and warn the caretaker that Mr Boo is coming on Saturday morning.

Yes! You've guessed it! We never see Mr Boo again, nor his three quid. The waiting room is still lickless. Despite his Awful Warnings, the doors, the central heating, the windows, the wiring and the skirting boards still soldier on.

Just one teeny-weeny detail, hardly worth mentioning. Last Sunday, the keyless surgery ceiling fell down.

DO IT YOURSELF LOMBROSO

I'm sitting in the chair, heels on the window sill, filling in my Pools Coupon wondering where the next patient is. In bounds my receptionist. "Guess what! Mrs Oy hasn't turned up for her appointment!"

"Didn't she cancel it?"

"Cancel! Ha! Since when do people bother to cancel dental appointments? They just don't come, didn't you know?" She backs out, frightened by my expression. "Shout if you want anything, I'm just showing the new girl the ropes."

The new girl is only temporary. She's been a receptionist to other dentists, but she's never come across a practice like mine. Through the partly open door I hear the sibilant instructions of ropes being shown. "...and he doesn't like patients who are 3.D."

"What's 3.D.?" the stand-in asks.

"People who are Dirty or Deaf or Daft. He goes raving mad if you take one on as a new patient."

"How d'you tell which is which?"

"Easy!" the regular girl confides. "You sift them out when they first come and ask for treatment. If they've got dirty heads when you open the door, then you have to say straight off that *he* can't manage. Anyone else is clean. He's caught enough fleas to last him a lifetime and *he* says he's old enough to be choosy now."

"Anyone without fleas gets an appointment?" the new girl asks doubtfully. She's obviously come from a practice where fauna don't exist.

"Oo, no!" The regular girl sounds horrified. "You haven't sorted them out *yet*. You've only got your clean ones, but if you have to shout to get them to understand what you're saying, then that counts as deaf. Don't let them in either; *he* goes mad if he has to shout everything he says, like 'Open wide, please' and they try to bite his fingers off. So that weeds out the deaf."

"So the rest are OK for an appointment?"

"*No!* Not *yet!* You still have to weed out the daft ones and this is the tricky bit. You see, most of his patients have to be a bit daft to start with, or they wouldn't put up with him. The way I tell is by looking at their faces. For example, don't ever, ever, give an appointment to anyone who's middle aged, with square faces and glasses."

"Why not?" The stand-in is amazed. (So am I!)

"Well — there's something about square faces and glasses in menopausal men and women which makes them blame *his* fillings for any pains they get afterwards — even aches in their damn bottoms. False teeth are worse, square face etcetera are never happy with *his* teeth. *He* goes mad."

"Who's left then, to let in?" The stand-in whispers. "I mean does he ever let in *any* new patients?"

"Oh *yes! He* gets on best with people who are as daft as *he* is. So, after I've said *No* to the dirty and the deaf and the double daft, I just glance at the eyes of whoever else comes. If they've got the same mad look that *he* has, then you *can* give them an appointment. Now, bend down and just look at Old Nutsy through the keyhole. See the mad look?"

Serves me right for eavesdropping.

I CAUGHT IT IN SPAIN –
or You know what I mean?

I approach the new patient with freshly dried fingers. "Now then," I fold up the towel. "What can I do for you?"

He holds a hand to his mouth and whispers "Can I speak to you alone?"

I wonder what sort of kink he has. I nod to the Surgery Attendant. She raises her eyebrows and, behind the patient's back, raises an archly warning finger, as she goes out.

"Well now?" I invite the patient to tell me about his problem.

Hand still in front of his mouth, he says "D'you remember a lady in a red hat that you treated for a mouth disease?"

I don't like the sound of ladies in red hats. "I'm very sorry, I don't remember *any* such lady." (Always deny everything.)

"Well, she lives up our street and she had a terrible mouth and you got rid of it for her."

I don't like the sound of "getting rid" of anything for ladies. "I treat a lot of sore mouths, you know."

He glances over his shoulder. "That's why I'm here."

I'm relieved. Two to one it's bad breath and his best friends have told him at last. "Is it," I pause for effect, "bad breath?"

He shakes his head. "I wish it was."

"What d'you mean? D'you actually *want* bad breath?"

"No!" He glances round again. "I think I've caught," he grimaces, "you know what I mean."

"Actually, I don't."

He wriggles impatiently. "You *must* know what I mean. I was in Spain last month, on holiday. All that wine and that," he nods again, "you know."

"Are you telling me that you have contracted a mouth infection?" I ask stiffly.

He whips a secret-keeping finger to his lips. "You know what it's like on holiday. I went a bit gay."

I stare at him wondering which bit it was. "Then you'd better tell me your symptoms hadn't you?"

He squirms, as if confession is being torn from his soul. "After I'd come back from Spain, I said '*Ah!*' in the mirror and I saw what I'd caught in Spain." He nods and swallows. "You know what I mean."

I don't know what he means, and I'm getting impatient with him. "Look here, just tell me *exactly* what's bothering you."

He looks round to make sure we're still alone. Then he thrusts out his tongue at me and tries to speak at the same time. Then he pulls his tongue in again. "Did you see it? Can you cure it? Isn't it awful? It's a punishment . . ."

"Relax!" I say. "You haven't caught anything at all. You've probably had this for years." (He emits a stifled scream.) "Lots of people have it, especially heavy smokers like you. It just doesn't matter at all."

"After what I told my wife about Spain, she'll never believe it doesn't matter. Just tell me the name for what I've got."

"Tell your wife that the dentist says you've got a harmless condition which we call Black Hairy Tongue." I wink at him. "You know what I mean."

Then he faints.

THE SOFT NUMBER —
or Always read the small print

"I'm not signing anything," says Mrs Er. (The receptionist points to the treatment form. "But you have to sign here to show that you authorise the dentist to look at your teeth.")

"I'm not signing *anything!*"

"What's going on out there?" I bellow through the open surgery door.

Mrs Er shouts back "I'm not signing *anything!* That's what's going on."

I stride into the receptionist's office. "But why won't you sign the form, you've always done it before?"

"I'm not signing anything," she sniffs, "because you haven't finished your last job properly."

"What last job?"

"Me false teeth." She fishes out her upper denture and waves it, steaming. "They're still loose." She thumbs the dripping thing back in.

The receptionist waves Mrs Er's record card at me. "The teeth are eight years old," she says, each syllable an acid drop.

"Oh don't you come that on me," says Mrs Er. "I complained about them the very moment you fitted them. And they've been loose ever since. Eight years of hell it's been."

I look at the record card. "Yes, you did complain. And you had an appointment for me to deal with the complaint. But you didn't come to that

appointment, did you? And you never told us you weren't coming, either. And you've never been back since, have you, despite eight years of hell?"

She's a bad loser. Appointment breakers usually are. "I couldn't hell-pit. I had the 'flu." After eight years, she switches on the instant recall memory of a bad attender.

"Let's forget all that," I suggest. "But now, after eight years, this is a different course of treatment. That's why you have to sign a new form."

31

"I'm not signing *anything*. You can't force me, neither."

(She's right, there. Not even on a desert island.)

"Nobody is forcing you. But I can't even look in your mouth if you won't sign on."

"Oh, give me the bloody thing!" She snatches at the pen. "Where d'you want my bloody name put?"

"Bloody here, madam," says the receptionist, pear-shaped vowelled and fireproofed by the knowledge that she at least can't be struck off for saying unto patients what patients say unto dentists.

Mrs Er looks as if she could spit. "Not so quick! I'm going to read every word of the small print first if you *don't* mind." Her finger finds its way through the maze of words. At last she braces herself to sign. "Hey!" She looks at me. "Will I have to pay anything this time?"

"You may have to."

She flings down the pen. "I'm not signing *anything*."

"Incidentally," I remind her. "You didn't finish reading all the small print. You missed this bit which says that broken appointments have to be paid for, even if they're eight years ago."

Tight-lipped, she snatches up the pen again. She signs on. Before we can stop her she's signed off too. "My husband wants you to look at his loose teeth and all," she says. "But you won't make *him* sign anything, mister. He's not a soft number like me."

32

BLOOD BROTHERS

"Shipping Agency on the 'phone," the receptionist tells me. "One of their deckhands is in terrible pain, and he's due to put to sea tonight. We've also just had a cancellation at four o'clock. What'll I say to them?"

"Tell them to send him at a quarter to, in case he's late arriving, like everyone else."

Naval quarter-to is quite unlike every other patient's timing; it occurs at a quarter to. Three bells. Doors open. "Navy's here!" says the receptionist. "Complete with escort vessel."

"Don't tell me they've sent two of them?" I'm getting (what they call round here) airyated.

She nods. "Only one for treatment, though. The other is to salvage the wreck after you've finished."

Ha-ha-ha and thank you very much. I tell her to up-anchor and pilot in the sailor. She soon sails back through the surgery close hauled. In tow is the blackest, jolliest-rogering sailor I've ever seen. Behind him shuffles a shipmate who says, "I'm not having anything done, I'm the official interpreter." He nods his head at the black sailor. "He's from Tatape — in the Pacific."

"Please ask him to take a seat."

The interpreter sounds like a recording being played backwards. "Ask him where the pain is," I say. There's more backward tape-recording. Tatape smiles broadly and points to a broken down tooth. "Please tell him that I'll have to take it out."

Tatape nods, so I take out the tooth. I say "All done now. Please ask him to rinse out."

The interpreter passes my signal on, and the patient tips half a glass of mouthwash into his mouth. I point to the basin and Tatape obliges in a single splash, like a geyser. His smile fades for a moment as he sees blood. His voice rumbles.

"Something wrong?" I ask.

"No," says the interpreter. "He says you've spilled his blood in a good cause and therefore are his blood brother."

"That's very civil of him," I answer uneasily. "Does it mean he now wants to spill some of mine?"

The signal is passed. Tatape roars with laughter and then rumbles again.

"What's he saying?"

"He says a little brotherly gift will do instead, and if he has the choice, he'd like that fat girl." The interpreter points at my buxom receptionist.

Tatape nods like mad. The receptionist screams.

D'you know, she never touches cakes nowadays, nor bread, nor potatoes, nor sugar, nor sweets. Some days I suspect she doesn't eat at all.

PERCY VERE

She comes into the surgery all middle aged, square-faced, and bespectacled. "Oh yes, I've persevered," she says, sitting in the chair. It's more an accusation than a confession. "But it's not a bit of use."

She thrusts an envelope into my hand, and I extract a set of false teeth. "I've persevered with those damn things till I'm blue in the face," she goes on. "Percy Vere, Percy Vere! [You'd think she was invoking Saint Percy Vere, the Patron Saint of False Teeth] That's all I've been doing for the past two years, Percy Vering. [All?] Are you sure you gave me the right teeth?"

"Let me try them in," I suggest. "I'll check them."

"You might find it easier if I took me old ones out first?" she suggests sourly. She tongues the old dentures into her hand, like a trainee bugler having a go at blowing reveille. "The things I've said about you." Her loose lips plop as she speaks. "Your ears must've been burning night and day."

I fit her offending dentures. "Now let's have a look."

She pushes my hands aside. "There's something wrong with the palate. Me top set keeps falling down."

"I see. Well, just let me . . ."

She pushes my hands away again. "Me bottom's all right, though."

36

I glance at her record card. "Wait a moment. I see that your teeth were an exact copy of that old set." I point to the old teeth resting on her lap, still steaming gently. "We'll soon see if you have been given the wrong dentures. Let's match them." I pick up the two top sets and hold them cheek by jowl. I get a sinking feeling. "The new one is shorter than the old ones. No wonder they're loose."

"You see!" she shouts with triumph. "I toljerso."

I turn up the plastic edge for a closer look. There's something wrong with it. I can see the flat facets of do-it-yourself grinding with a nail-file, or perhaps the emery of a match box. "Hello! You've been having a file at this, yourself, haven't you? You've had a go at it."

She glares at me as if I'd accused her of How's Your Father or even You Know What. "I *beg* your pardon."

"Someone's filed the back of the denture away. It's ruined the suction."

"Utter nonsense."

I resist the urge to hit her. "Just look for yourself." I point, finger trembling with anger. "That back end has been cut off. Look at all those grooves. It may be utter nonsense to you, but it looks like nail-file to me." A thought crosses my mind. "Unless it was one of those saw-edged bread-knives."

No, I believe her too. It never is me who does it. It's probably St. Percy Vere, working by remote control.

38

EVER SINCE YOU . . . (and other greetings)

When a patient comes in and starts off with "*Ever since you . . .*" I know it means that my last treatment is about to be held responsible for absolutely any bodily disorder which happened to turn up afterwards.

1. *Ever since* you did that filling, I've had dandruff.
2. *Ever since* you took that tooth out I've had the hear-ache (or the ear-hake or, if the patient is Welsh, the year-ache).
3. *Ever since* you scraped the enamel off my teeth, not one morsel of food has passed my lips! (Which means, I suppose, that they are feeding their fourteen-stone skeletons by venous drip, or by shoving bacon and egg up their nostrils or up somewhere else.)

Now, all dentists have their Mrs Trickie. She's a patient who never needs a six-monthly reminder because she's always coming back with a chip broken off this, or an ache in that, or a vague pain which takes all of an hour on the busiest day of the week — and still defies diagnosis.

Well — I thought I'd got rid of my Mrs Trickie when she emigrated to Tasmania. Even then, at the last minute she had to be pushed in for a quick look because *ever since* . . . something or other that I'd done. I thought I'd finished with her. But, six months later, in comes Mrs T to say she's back from Tasmania for just two days and just happens to be passing the surgery, and must see her pommie-bastard dentist (they learn fast do these emigrants) because ever since she left Pom-land she's been suffering. Actually — for a change, there *is* a small hole in a tooth, so I fill it. *I must be mad.*

A day later, she rings from London Airport to say that *ever since* I filled her tooth she's had neuralgia. I prescribe by telephone. Then her plane is delayed by a bomb scare. So she rings three hours later to say that, *ever since* I told her what to do with her neuralgia, her Old Trouble has come on too. So I treat that by 'phone.

She sends a complaining telegram from Singapore, an express letter from Melbourne and an (unstamped, very expensive) ultimatum from Hobart saying "*Ever since* I've been under you, I've never felt anything even approaching satisfaction, so I intend to write your name in black all over Tasmania."

Whilst shoving the correspondence into her record card, my receptionist discovers that, *ever since* Mrs Trickie's been under me, she's never paid her bill. (A few more like that and they'll be writing my name in red all over my bank account — and/or, dare I say it, Caries St.)

I send her a bill in an unstamped, very expensive envelope.

That's the end of my pommie-bastard story because, cobber and bluey, *ever since* then, I've not heard a word from her.

IMMEDIATE ACTION —
or What's the first thing you do when . . .

On grandpa's second day at school, a golden-curled girlie minced up to him, trembling her petalled fingers in his face. "What's the first thing you'd do if I asked you to smell cheese?" she asked.

Always a gentleman, he shook his head.

"Smell this instead," she shouted, punching him on the nose.

The same thing happened to my father, to me and to my children. Yet you can't blame children for preserving the folk-lore of "What's the first thing" — we all do it. When I learned to drive, the ritual, clever question was, "What's the first thing you do before driving off?" Then once, in a rain-soaked bivouac, my platoon sergeant kept us guessing for hours with "What's the first thing you do when you pick up your rifle." The Army had a lot of quick answers to many similar questions, and they used to call it Yer Immediate Action. Had I remembered my sergeant's answer ("Make sure you're not holding someone else's"), then life in these piping days would have been much easier for me. You see, I still tend to pop false teeth into patients' mouths without checking the names first.

For example, Mrs Er came in to have some new dentures fitted, and stupid-old-fool-me fits her up so that her correct top set is chewing on somebody else's bottom. Very painful. Worse still, off she goes on a Mediterranean cruise.

I don't even realise my mistake until poor old
Mr Somebody Else arrives for his new teeth and **takes**

immediate exception to the fit of Mrs Er's bottom. So, I ask myself, "What's Yer Immediate Action? What's the first thing you do when you fit the wrong teeth?" And the answer is, I withdraw the teeth "for adjustment" — for what my mechanics call a time-wasting "bench-rest", to give the impression that something is being done whilst I think what the hell *can* I do.

Three weeks later, back comes Mrs Er, sun-tanned, fit and two stones lighter through not eating properly. "These new teeth," she says. "They've been tearing my gums to shreds."

"Ah yes!" I try to look all-knowing. "I *did* make the bottom set a *very* special fit for good stability and all that sort of thing. Just let me have it and I'll ease it off a bit." I hold out my hand and poise myself to scuttle off into the work room and do a quick change with the correct lower denture, which is asleep in a basin of water, enjoying its "bench rest".

She hands me her top set. I wave it aside. "Not that one. Give me the lower."

"What for?" she asks. "It's my top that's killing me. My bottom is absolutely smashing, and I'm not going to let you fiddle with it."

D'you know, I don't think there's *any* of Yer Immediate Action for a crisis like this. I reckon I'd just better make a new lower denture for poor, old, highly abusive Mr Somebody Else, before he asks me if I'd like to smell cheese.

A KID FOR TWO TEETH OUT

"Whatever happens to our city in July and August every year?" my receptionist asks. "They don't have summer holidays, they have toothache."

Over a radius of what seems like twenty miles, come July and August, if a tooth aches or a face swells, it seems to end up at my surgery door. "That's the seventh," the receptionist intones. "All wanting teeth out."

"You *didn't* . . ."

"Don't worry," she soothes me. "When I showed them the waiting room, they all changed their minds. It's stacked to the ceiling with people. They're even sitting on each other's knees."

"Is one of them by any chance the next customer?"

She laughs, short, hard and bitter. "Yes. He's been waiting forty minutes."

"Then who are these people sitting on his knee?"

She counts on her hand, like "Green grow the rushes — *ho*." "Four teeth a-aching, three facial swellings, two dentures rubbing, and one with a disease which her sister (married to a dental technician who knows) diagnoses as diarrhoea of the gums. That makes ten waiting to be fitted in."

My two word answer is drowned by the doorbell. She goes to answer it. Suddenly, she's screaming, and I rush to the rescue. She's pinned to the wall by a wagging finger which threatens her throat. Attached to the finger is a red-faced, furious woman from whose other hand dangles a small, wide-eyed child. "Tell him it's only a kid for two bloody teeth out!" she's yelling. Then, she turns on me. "It's an emergency! This kid's had us up all night, so his dad says you get him done girl or don't bloody come home again."

"But it's impossible," I say, pointing to the waiting room.

"Oh no it's *not* impossible, mister," she flings back. "Just do him first, before that effin lot. He only wants a bit of gas, don't you?" She shakes the hanging child as if it were a wet bathing costume. "And he's had the ache for weeks and weeks," she adds, nodding.

"Weeks and weeks!" says a voice from the waiting room. "Then he can wait an effin bit longer! I was effin here before effin you *and* your effin kid."

"Tell you what," I suggest. "If you bring your little boy back tomorrow morning, I'll see him first thing."

"Eff off you," she answers graciously. "That's the trouble with your sort. You stay at home making effin money whilst all the proper dentists go on their effin holidays."

"Madam!" I try to climb on my high horse.

"Don't you madam me!" She waggles her finger at my throat. "Tomorrow morning I can take him to see his *own* dentist. He's coming back from effin Majorca tonight." She makes a gesture which one may charitably interpret as 'a fig for your services'. She addresses the waiting room. "And you lot! The effin same!" It's a fig for them too.

I send for next year's diary, which arrived last week. I cross out the two whole months of July and August. "Effing staff holidays," I tell the receptionist.

Well — an eff in time, saves nine.

SOCIETY DINNER

Evenings for the dentist of 50+ tend to be a time for lying back, gathering the strength to go to bed so that next morning, half charged, he can carry on (like the Oozlum Bird) grinding his helical way downhill until he disappears up his own pension — if he lives that long.

But sometimes he is tempted by the fleshpots, and one day I find myself hooked by an invitation to attend a Dental Society Dinner *with wines*. Although I've long forgotten the name of the Greek Father of Dentistry, the name of Lynch-Bages is still graven, like Calais, on my palate. For the right wine, I'm even willing to shake my patched dinner jacket free of its paradichlorbenzene. The miniature medals tell me it was last worn twenty-three years ago, for a regimental dinner.

"Tee Hee!" says my wife, mimicking those mocking characters in our children's comics. "Those wide lapels and baggy pants! You look like a gangster! Hello Al, how's Frank Nitti?"

I examine my reflection in our wardrobe mirror. I'm George Raft to a T (or is it an R — assuming you remember him). "Don't care! It's such a long time since I went to a Dental Society Dinner that nobody'll recognise me anyway."

7.30 for 8.00 says the invitation. I stroll into the hotel lounge, finger gun-barrelling in my jacket pocket, like George Raft. I glance around looking for

a face familiar enough to shake hands with, but there isn't one. Even The Knob wearing a medalled cordon bleu around his neck is a complete stranger. Dentists' lady-wives (I've never met the other sort, actually) stand around, elbows bent, glass in hand, chatting double-forte and roaring with laughter at inane comments they wouldn't have giggled at, earlier in the day. Everyone greets everyone with a "What'll you have?" Everyone, that is, except me and poor old George Raft who smiles bravely back from each peach-coloured wall mirror.

Arms folded, I stand at the back on tip-toe. I'm casting my gaze around in the hope of hooking and landing someone's passing eye. Mrs Cordon Bleu suddenly smiles at me. I don't recognise her, but I smile back. She waves her fingers at me, delicately, as if shaking off some fluff.

I wave back still smiling, wondering who she can be.

She turns her hand and beckons.

I point to my old silk facings and raise my eyebrows in question. She nods.

George Raft and I walk forward, expecting to be officially presented to the President of our Learned Society. At a range of three yards, up comes my hand to be shaken.

But my offer is ignored. "Ah! There you are at last!" says Mrs President. "May I have another sweet sherry please, *waiter!*"

MENOPAUSAL DYSPHAGIA –
or The not-so-grand-climacteric

Mrs Er is whispering to the receptionist, woman to woman ". . . and I had a sudden hot flush, and I couldn't even swallow the mouthful of gin." From the back of the surgery, she suddenly shouts at me "*He's Percy!* His name's *Percy* and you *always* call Tommy! I've got another bone to pick with you and all!" she thunders on, her face getting redder and redder. "Why wouldn't you see our John last Thursday, eh?"

I'm wondering what's hit me. I don't remember Our John, or what happened last Thursday, either.

"I'm not surprised you're struck dumb all of a sudden," she goes on, giving me no time to answer. "Just tell me this. How would you like it if it happened to you?"

Happen? Does she mean how would I like it if I couldn't swallow my gin? As happened to her? I'd better parley. 'I'm sorry, but I honestly don't remember a thing about your gin — er — I mean your John."

She purses her lips. "And I'm not surprised, after the way you treated him last Thursday."

My receptionist is sitting, coolly riding out the storm. I ask her, "What's this all about?"

"Johnny Er didn't keep his appointment last Monday. He turned up on Thursday without a word of explanation and wanted to make a fresh appointment. So I gave him one."

"There you are!" Mrs Er shouts in triumph. "You wouldn't treat him, just like I said."

"But he only came to make a new appointment. . ."

Unimpressed, Mrs Er attacks from another angle. "And another thing! I've been bringing every single one of my children to you for years and all you ever do is fill their teeth."

I am suddenly in that dream world of shocked surprise, as if my old car had refused petrol, demanding water instead, or even castor oil. "But didn't you want their teeth filled?" (Remind me to re-read Kafka.) My ageing senses threaten to drop-out. I hear myself asking, with a faint tremor, "If you don't want your little boy's teeth filled, then what have you brought him for today?"

"Oh! So it's like that then, is it?" She snaps back, standing up. "We'd better go somewhere else. Come on, Percy. We're *not* wanted *here*." Suddenly, her red face strikes its colours and up goes the white-cheeked flag of truce. "I'm so sorry," she whispers. "Sometimes I don't know what I'm saying. It's *the change*."

Twice as relieved as Mafeking, I suggest that another appointment would suit us all, especially me (and Kafka). I act the Compleate Professional Manne and say "Pish" and "Pshaw" and all the other words which really mean why should I share the sufferings of someone else's menopause especially when I'm busy coping with my own.

Armed with a fresh appointment, Mrs Er sails away. She fires a last Parthain shaft. "You older men just don't know how damn lucky you are."

I reckon that when the Government or Womens' Lib start equalising men and women, they ought to insert a clause making menopause for women conditional upon them allowing men to have womenopause. If that doesn't work, then I'd forbid the damn thing altogether. (And that includes lunatics, peers and consenting adults, too.)

LIFE INSURANCE –
or And he who shouts loudest lives longest

Dog-tired is nothing to how a dentist feels when he reaches the end of a working day. Sore-headed bears are often sweet-tempered by comparison with middle-aged G.Ps at going-home-time. Yet, bottle up your feelings (says the doctor) and you're heading for a coronary. Shout! He says. Let it froth away in shouting, and the worst you'll get is laryngitis (and a reputation for being a nut-case).

We're ready to go home. The receptionist runs through her last cockpit check. Steriliser off. Tools away. Main switch off. Burglar alarm on. Intercom out. Documents in. Drug-cupboard locked.

There's someone kicking hell out of the front door. I'm sounding a view halloo that would awaken both John Peel and St Apollonia from their beds. "The way you shout!" the receptionist says. "Anyone would think you *were* mad, even if it does make you feel better." Then, off she goes to see who wants our services so late in the day.

There's whispering in the passageway. Back she comes. "There's a man who wants to see you personally." She waves a defensive hand at me. "Please don't start yelling. It's something to do with insurance."

I do yell at her. "You go straight back and tell him from me," I'm shouting all tight throat and clangy voice, like Sir Laurence Olivier "upon Saint

Crispin's Da-a-a-a-a-y". "Go and tell him he's thirty years too late. I'm cashing in my insurances next month and I don't want any new ones."

The poor receptionist hobbles away with my message. She's tired too, and she'd also like the self-employed perk of finding relief in shouting double forte, ad lib. But she's more lady than I am gentleman. I hear her whispering in the passage. I hear the rustle of proposal forms being clicked back into a creaking brief case. I hear departing footsteps and the thump of a slammed front door. Back she comes, tired but triumphant. "He's gone. You can relax."

"Well done, girl!" I'm buttoning up my overcoat. "How d'you manage it so quickly?"

"I just told him he was wasting his time. I told him you'd been turned down by three life insurance companies on grounds of insanity. After hearing all your bellowing, he believed it."

I'm bellowing again.

"Now now!" she says gently. "One more shout and you'll have me believing you're mad too. Remember, I've only been with you twenty-three years, and I'm not sure we're suited yet."

Of course, I have to laugh then. For one thing, it's easier on the throat than shouting.